whíst
anɒ sí

by Eamonn Jordan

OSSIAN

Whistle and Sing, Book One

Originally Published in 1974

Acknowledgements

For helping in so many ways . . . Brigid McCann, B.A., Eileen Fitzpatrick,
Pat McCabe, Jim Creany, Eithne McLoughlin, Jerry Garvey, Leslie Bingham,
Malachy Comac, Seamus McMahon, Roisín White, Fr. Tom McConville,
Eithne Vallely, Kieran McCann and Deirdre Marley of Ceoltóirí Phort an Dúnáin,
Comhaltas Ceoltóirí Éireann, The National Museum of Ireland,
The Ulster Museum, The O'Mealy Trust and the Arts Council of Northern Ireland
– and all those patient people not mentioned who counselled, advised, bullied and
helped to bring this book to fruition.

The author is indebted to Rita McEvoy, B.A. and Danny McQuillan for invaluable
help in selecting, transcibing and arranging the contents.

Printed by Lee Press, Cork

Ossian Publications
P.O.Box 84, Cork, Ireland
ossian@iol.ie

Ossian OMB 110   ISBN 1 900428 00 8

Contents

PATRICK QUINN

Patrick Quinn, the Portadown harper, was a pupil of Patrick Lyndon of the Fews, Co. Armagh. Lyndon was acquainted with O'Carolan. Quinn was one of the harpers at the Belfast Harp Festival of 1792 and was selected to play at the O'Carolan Commemoration Meeting of musicians in Dublin in 1809.

INTRODUCTION

We remember being somewhat startled at hearing a judge at a Fleadh-Cheoil declare that a competitor's entry, a popular air, was too well-known to be a suitable entry for a Fleadh! Whilst it is possible to sympathise with the judge, who had probably heard that song a thousand times, it is all to easy to forget that all our music becomes new to each new generation and has to be taught anew.

We have, in our Irish music, one the Western world's richest treasuries. It is taken for granted that each new generation will carry on the tradition. Faced with the impact of today's mass media this assumption is folly of the highest order. Despite the efforts of a few interested organisations and dedicated individuals no real effort is being made at national level to teach that which is uniquely ours.

Often, those least qualified to do so, take up the burden, (if that term can even apply to that which is loved) and long for some guidance.

With this in mind, the newcomer to Irish music, and we hope, the more experienced player too, will find in these pages a carefully selected range of songs, airs and dance music. Songs in Irish and English, popular reels and jigs, old favourites and new, are all here.

For the beginner, hints and tips on music and the more popular instruments are given. The first section of the book consists of simple, easily played tunes and songs. To aid the beginner, and the teacher also, most of the basic musical theory necessary is given in this section. Additional information appears throughout the book

For teaching purposes, all tunes have numbered bars, and heavy bar lines indicate the different parts of the tunes. For interest's sake, the book has been arranged into a number of sections separated by songs. In avoiding the usual massing of reels, jigs, etc., together we hope that the beginner will browse right through the book. So, for this reason also, easy airs can be found right to the last pages.

Most of the tunes have been arranged with the 'D' whistle in mind. It is the ideal beginner's instrument and additional music is available for it. We recommend the 'Generation' brand.

Finally, we stress the importance of listening to good players in order to acquire a correct style. Whilst a great deal of care has been taken to ensure that the versions given are those commonly played it must be pointed out that the traditional style is an art form which cannot wholly be learnt from the information provided in written music.

Teachers should make every effort to ensure that pupils are frequently in contact with the living musical tradition. In writing this book the author was time and time again overwhelmed by the lengths to which traditional musicians were willing to go to be of assistance.

Eamonn Jordan
Portadown,
1974.

The Whistle

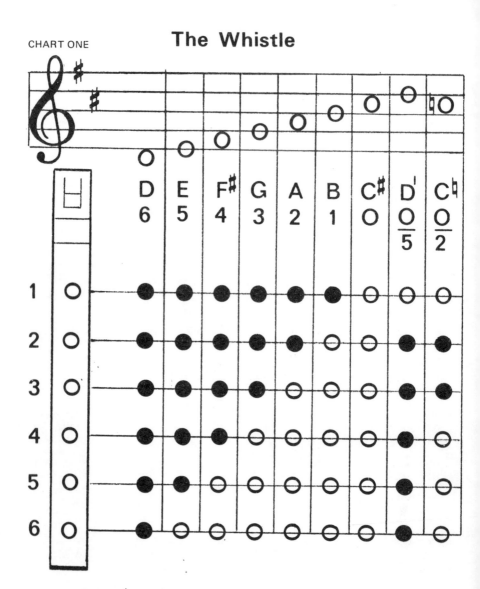

The first three fingers of the left hand cover holes   1, 2 and 3.
The first three fingers of the right hand cover holes   4, 5 and 6.
Thus six fingers on gives 'D', 5 fingers on gives 'E' etc.
'D' with six fingers is the hardest to get right. Make sure the holes are covered properly and breathe gently into the whistle D', the octave, is produced by having all fingers down except the top finger of the left hand, hence, 0-five. To get 0-two, C natural, now remove the three fingers of the right hand, 4, 5 and 6, keeping 2 and 3 on.

Start by blowing B1, A2, G3, F4, E5 and the harder D6 last.

1

Music for Beginners

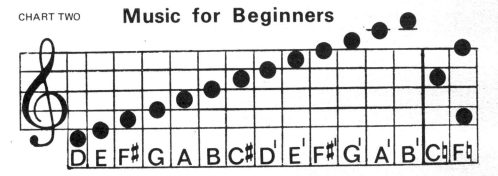

Almost all of the tunes in this book and indeed, almost all of our Irish traditional music, can be played using the sixteen notes above.
There are only seven different notes — D. E. F. G. A. B. C.

The notes in the spaces are	**F. A. C. E.**
The notes on the lines are	**E. G. B. D. F.**
Below the lines (or stave) is	**D.**
Above the stave are	**G. A. B.**

You can remember the notes in the spaces by thinking of the word **'FACE!'** And the notes on the lines by the rhyme **'Every Good Boy Deserves Favour!'**

You will notice that the notes go up like steps of stairs! First we have D. E. F♯ G. A. B. C♯ followed on by D'. E'. F♯' G'. A'. B'. Each of the last group of notes is said to be an octave (eight notes) higher than the same note in the first group. Count for yourself. It is very easy to play the higher **octave notes** on the 'D' whistle, use the same fingering for the second octave as for the first. but blow a **little** harder! The octave notes are marked D' ('D' one), E' ('E' one) etc.

There are three other notes at the right hand side of chart two, they are **C natural (C♮), F natural (F♮)** and the **Octave of F♮ .** A sharp sign ♯ raises a note half a tone and a natural ♮ brings it back again.

When we play D. E. F♯ G. A. B. C♯ D' this is called the 'D' scale. If we played G. A. B. C♮ D'. E'. F♯'G'. we would call it the 'G' scale. Almost all Irish dance music is played in these scales or keys and all of these notes are on the 'D' whistle. Which makes it very handy!
To indicate the scale music is marked as follows. **Play these now!**

CHART THREE

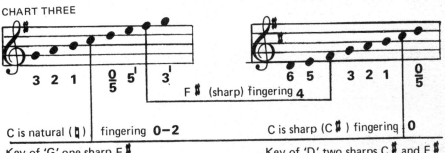

C is natural (♮)	fingering **0-2**	C is sharp (C♯) fingering	**0**
Key of 'G' one sharp F♯		Key of 'D' two sharps C♯ and F♯	

More Music for Beginners

The basic idea of music is to give, in written form, the 'story' of a tune. Let us take a look, therefore, at the 'story' of the **'Belfast Polka'** and see what we can discover!

A First Tune

One	It is divided by bar lines into eight bars of music. Each of these bars or groups of notes has the same number of beats and the strongest beat comes at the beginning of a bar.
Two	This is the sign for the 'G' clef. At the moment it is not important. It names the second line 'G'.
Three	The sharp sign ♯ on the top line is the **'Key Signature.'** It tells us that this tune is in the key of 'G' (chart 3) with 'F' sharp, fingering 4 and 'C' natural, fingering 0-2.
Four	2/4 is the **'Time Signature'** telling us that this tune has two beats to a bar and four quavers to a bar.
Five	The two dots : at the end mean 'play this part twice '
Six	The fingering for the whistle is given for each bar. Now try this tune, using the whistle chart one if you get stuck!
Seven	7 at the end of bar four is a quaver rest.

Now we need to know the different types of notes,

So here are the most common, assuming a crochet has one beat.

CHART FOUR

◯ = 4 BEATS	◗ = 2 BEATS	● = 1 BEAT	● = ½ BEAT	● = ¼ BEAT
SEMI-BREVE	MINIM	CROCHET	QUAVER	SEMI-QUAVER

3

Hints and Tips

It is important to realise that the **relationship** between the different notes is **always** the same. In the time taken to play one minim you could play two crochets or four quavers, etc.

CHART FIVE

ONE MINIM = TWO CROCHETS = FOUR QUAVERS = EIGHT SEMI-QUAVERS

Notice that quavers and semi-quavers can be written two ways!

Use table 5 above together with table four and check that all the bars in table 5 have the same number of beats.

CHART SIX

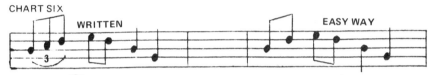

The triplet, 3, three notes played in the time of two, can be simplified by leaving out the middle note. Then replacing it when the beginner has got the timing of the bar right.

CHART SEVEN

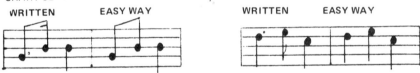

A dot after a note in creases its value by half. It is often followed by a shortened note as shown above and for the beginner can be simplified as shown above.

Time Signatures!

Tell us about the speed and rhythm of a tune. At first, for a beginner, the rhythm of a dance is best learnt by listening to the tunes being played, live or on radio, television, tape or records. Here are some examples of time signatures and their uses. Hornpipes are usually timed like reels. Songs can be in any time!

CHART EIGHT

REELS		SONGS		JIGS		SLIP JIGS	
C or $\frac{4}{4}$	Four Beats To A Bar	$\frac{3}{4}$	Three Beats To A Bar	$\frac{6}{8}$	Two Dotted Beats To A Bar	$\frac{9}{8}$	Three Dotted Beats To A Bar.
4 Crochets To A Bar		3 Crochets To a Bar		6 Quavers To A Bar		Nine Quavers To A Bar	
Common Time		Three Four Time		Six Eight Time		Nine Eight Time	

4

Óró Sé Do Bheatha 'Bhaile

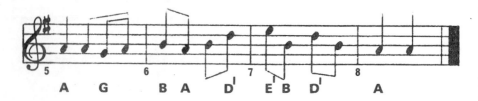

Curfá:

Óró! sé do bheatha 'bhaile!
Óró! sé do bheatha 'bhaile!
Óró! sé do bheatha 'bhaile!
Anois ar theacht an tsamhraidh.

Sé do bheatha! a bhean ba léanmhar!
B'é ár gcreach tú bheith i ngéibhinn,
Do dhúiche bhreá·i seilbh méirleach
'S tú díolta leis na Gallaibh.

Curfá.

Tá Gráinne Mhaol ag teacht thar sáile,
Óglaigh armtha léi mar gharda;
Gaeil iad féin 's ní Gaill ná Spáinnigh,
'S cuirfid ruaig ar Ghallaibh.

Curfá.

A bhuí le Rí na bhfeart go bhfeiceam,
Muna mbeam beo 'na dhiaidh ach seachtain,
Gráinne Mhaol agus míle gaiscíoch
Ag fógairt fáin ar Ghallaibh.

Curfá.

Bheir Mi Ó

GB B D' E' B G B D' E' B A D E

F G A D' E D' E G G

Curfá:

Bheir mí óró, bhean ó
Bheir mí óró ó bhean í,
Bheir mí óró ó hó
Tá mę brónach 's tú i m' dhíth.

'S iomaí oíche fliuch is fuar
Thug mé cuairt is mé liom féin
Nó go ráinig mé san áit
Mar a raibh grá geal mo chléibh.

Curfá.

I mo chláirseach ní raibh ceol
I mo mheoraibh ní raibh brí,
Nó gur luaigh tú do rún
'S fuair mé eolas ar mo dhán.

Curfá.

'Bheir Mí Ó' deals, as do many songs, with the love of a man for a woman. It tells us that he lost his gift for music in the loneliness of his longing for her, until she said her destiny was with him.

This is one of the loveliest of songs of Scottish Gaelic origin. Most of these songs are well known to Irish speakers, emphasising the links between the Celtic nations.

Remember!

Notes on the lines,   E. G. B. D. F.
Notes in the spaces,   F. A. C. E.
Notes on the whistle,   D.6, E.5, F.4, G.3, A.2, B.1, C Natural 0-2, D' 0-5.
This tune is in key G. (F is sharp).

6

Belfast Polka

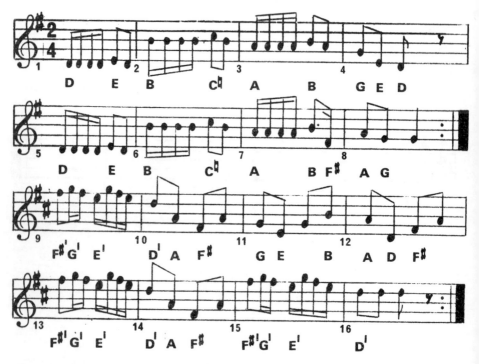

Notice that the first part, bars 1 - 8, has one sharp, 'F,' and is in the key of 'G.' The second part, bars 9 - 16, has two sharps as its key signature and is in the key of 'D'. Listen to the effect as the tune changes key. Listen too, to the way the even numbered bars answer back the odd numbered bars in part one.

The first part of this tune is very suitable for a beginners class. In Ceoltóirí Phort an Dúnáin we have great fun with it! Here's how we do it.

Divide the class into four groups, 'A,' 'B,' 'C,' 'D.' Group 'A' takes bar one, group 'B' bar two, group 'C' bar three and group 'D' bar four.

Then group 'A' follows with bar five, 'B' with six, 'C' with seven and group 'D' finishes with bar eight.

Playing in sequence like this, groups 'A' and 'B' have only two notes each to play, groups 'C' three different notes and group 'D' four different notes.

Having mastered each, the groups can be switched around until everyone knows the whole tune.

Notes on the lines. E. G. B. D. F. Notes in the spaces. F. A. C. E.

Whistle Fingering. D is 6, E is 5, F is 4, G is 3, A is 2, B is 1, C is 0-2, C sharp is 0, D' is 0-5.

Key 'G', first part of tune, has one sharp, 'F' fingering 4. Finger C Natural 0-2.

Key 'D' second part of tune has two sharps, 'F' and 'C.' Finger 'C' sharp 'O'.

7

Don Oiche Ud i mBeithil

A CHRISTMAS CAROL

Now try this, using the notes at the bottom of Page 7 as a guide. For the octave
notes, don't forget to blow a little harder! There are no sharps so 'C' is natural,
0-2.

Don oíche úd i mBeithil, beidh tagairt ag grian go brách
Don oíche úd i mBeithil go dtáinig an briathar slán,
Tá gríosghrua ar spéarthaibh 's an talamh 'na chlúdach bán;
Féach Íosagán sa chléibhín, 's an mhaighdean á dhiúl le grá.

Ar leacain lom an tsléibhe go nglacann na haoirí scáth
Nuair in oscailt ghil na spéire tá teachtaire Dé ar fáil;
Céad glóire anois don Athair i bhFlaitheasaibh thuas go hard!
Is feasta fós ar talamh d'fhearaibh dea-mhéin síocháin!

This beautiful tune is one of the few Irish Christmas carols to come down to us.
Compare the sweet plaintiveness of its modal character with the more 'modern'
or western sound of the 'Belfast Polka.' Notice that bar 12 contains the note 'E'
and the note 'E' ' the octave. Remember to play these high notes by blowing a
little harder. See notes on octaves Page 2.

8

Níl Sé 'na Lá

This one is very easy! Use the notes at the bottom of the page as a guide. Notice the key signature. Two sharps, 'F,' fingering 4 and 'C' fingering O, Key 'D'.

Chuaigh mé isteach i dteach aréir,
A's d'iarr mé cáirt ar bhean a' leanna;
'Sé dúirt sí liom; "Ní bhfaighidh tú deor,
Buail an bóthar a's gabh n a bhaile."

Curfá:

Níl sé 'na lá, nil a ghrá
Níl sé 'na lá, ná baol ar maidin,
Níl sé 'na lá 's ní bheidh go fóill
Solas ard atá sa ghealaigh.

Curfá.

Chuir mé féin mo lámh 'mo phoc',
Is d'iarr mé briseadh coróin' uirthi,
'S é dúirt sí liom: "Buail a' bord
A's bí ag ól anseo go maidin."

Curfá.

"Éirigh 'do shuí, a fhir a' tí,
Cuir ort do bhríste a's do hata,
Go gcoinní tú ceol leis a' duine chóir,
A bheas ag ól anseo go maidin.

Curfá.

You should by now have memorised these, but here they are again! This simple, basic information lets you play any tune. Learn these.

Notes on the lines	E. G. B. D. F.
In the spaces	F. A. C. E.
On the whistle	D6. E5. F sharp 4. G3. A2. B1. C 0-2, C sharp 0. D' 0-5.

Nach mise féin an fear gan chéill
A d'fhág mo chíos i mo scornaigh;
D'fhág mé léan orm féin,
Is d'fhág mé séan ar dhaoine eile.

Curfá.

Who'll Come Fight in the Snow?

SLIP JIG

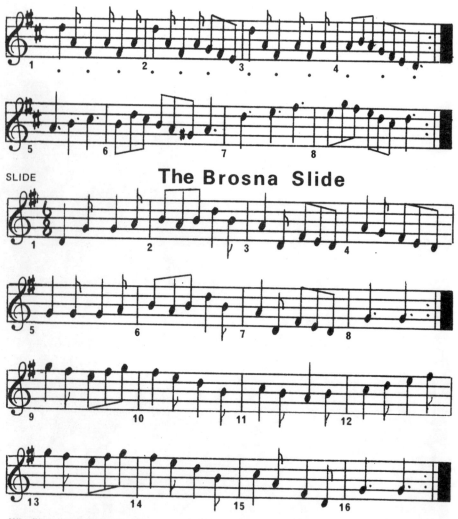

The Brosna Slide

SLIDE

Who'll come fight in the snow. Key 'D'.

Slip jigs have three emphasised beats in a bar. We have placed dots beneath the first line of music to indicate where the beat comes. This beautiful little tune should be played somewhat slower than usual for maximum effect. It is not at all difficult and is a firm children's favourite.

Bar 6 has G sharp. Play this with fingering three, half covering the third hole, and covering the first and second.

Brosna Slide:

The slide is a rarity in the north of Ireland but is danced with great vigour in Kerry. To say 'play this tune fast and furious' might be going too far, but you have the idea!

11

The Sweets of May

This is a very popular dance in Co. Armagh. The first part is usually played three times. And the first note 'F sharp' with its pause only used at the start.

Steps and figures are given in 'The Irish Folk-Dance Book' book two, by Peadar O'Rafferty and published by Patterson's publications Ltd.

Key G. All 'F's are sharp. (On the 'D' whistle they are sharp anyway!)
On the Lines. E. G. B. D. F.
In the spaces. F. A. C. E.
Remember D6. E5. F4. G3. A2. B1. C 0-2. C sharp 0. D' 0-5.

Siún Ní Dhuibhir

D'éirigh mé 'r maidin a tharraingt chun aonaigh mhóir,
A dhíol 's a cheannacht mar dhéanfadh mo dhaoine romham;
Bhuail tart ar a' bhealach mé 's shuigh mise síos a dh'ól,
'S le Siún Ní Dhuibhir gur ól mise luach na mbróg.

A Shiún Ní Dhuibhir an miste leat mé bheith tinn?
Mo bhrón 's mo mhilleadh má's miste liom tú 'bheith i gcill;
Brointe   muilte bheith scileadh ar chúl do chinn,
Ach cead a bheith in Iorras go dtara síol Éabh 'un cinn.

A Shiún Ní Dhuibir 's tú bun agus barr mo scéil;
Ar mhná na cruinne go dtug sise 'n báire léi
Le gile le finne le mais' is le dhá dtrian scéimh,
'S nach mise 'n trua Mhuire bheith scaradh amárach léi.

Thiar in Iorras tá searc agus grá mo chléibh,
Planda 'n linbh a d' eitigh mo phósadh inné;
Beir scéala uaim chuici má thug mise póg dá béal,
Go dtabharfainn di tuilleadh dá gcuirfeadh siad bólacht léi.

Beir scéala uaim chuige go dearfa nach bpósaim é,
Ó chuala mise gur chuir sé le bólacht mé;
Nuair nach bhfuil agamsa maoin nó mórán spré,
Bíodh a rogha bean aige 's beidh mise 'r mo chomhairle féin.

Transposing

OLD KEY	G	A	B	C	D	E	F#	G
NEW KEY	D	E	F#	G	A	B	C#	D
do		C	D	E	F	G	A	B	C
do		Bb	C	D	Eb	F	G	A	Bb

In this book we have tried to keep the songs in keys both easily sung and playable on the 'D' whistle. That is not always possible so some songs may have a low note or two that the 'D' whistle doesn't play.

Normally, in this case, the whistle player plays the whole tune one octave up, or seeks alternative notes. We talked about octaves on page two.

On the other hand, as voices vary from singer to singer, some singers might wish to use a lower key than we have chosen. There is nothing difficult about writing a tune out in a different key. All you need is a pencil, some ruled paper and the chart above!

For example, we assume the tune you wish to change is written in the key of 'G' and you wish to change it to key 'D' then, using the chart, 'E' in key 'G' would become 'B' in key 'D' and so on. Crochets are still crochets, etc. and the only other thing to change is the key signature. ('D' has two sharps).

Of course the table will work just as well going from 'D' to 'G', or 'Bb' to 'D', or 'C' to 'G' etc.

The whistle player normally uses a whistle pitched in the key he wishes to transpose to. See note three, page 22.

Violins, accordians, banjos, etc. can easily change key. For simplicity's sake the charts in this book only give details of the keys of 'G' and 'D' for these instruments. But the player will quickly learn additional scales as he becomes more proficient.

Practice

The tunes in section one were arranged with the beginner in mind. With the hints and tips given, and with **PRACTICE** the beginner should now be able to read music, even if slowly.

The following pages introduce reels and hornpipes, and have some more difficult songs songs, polkas and airs. But there are many easy pieces too, as a browse over the pages will show. Hard tunes become easy when played slowly!

It is a fact that most tunes have a difficult bar or two. Do not be tempted to play quickly over the easy parts and then stumble over the difficult rhythm. Instead, play the whole tune at a speed which lets you fit the awkward notes in smoothly. When you can do this, then speed up gradually.

PRACTISE DAILY, even if only for a short while. Don't waste time whilst practising, concentrate on overcoming some difficulty, or on memorising a particular air.

A short concentrated, daily practice is of far more value than a longer, careless one twice a week!

PHRASING

As well as having a certain number of beats per bar, most Irish melodies are divided into phrases of two bars. Often, the last note or two of these two bar phrases carries the tune into the next phrase.

It is important to be able to pick out these phrases. The rhythm of a reel and the flow of a song alike depend on proper phrasing.

Let us look at the Carol on Page 8. A line is given here.

CHART TEN

Play this over, pausing at the end of each phrase.

Here, the phrase of bars one and two ends on the long 'A' in the middle of bar two. The last 'A' in bar two starts the phrase consisting of bars three and four. This in turn ends on the 'G' in bar four. The 'E' in bar four starts the next phrase and so on.

Look for this type of construction in reels, and in other dances and songs. Knowing this will help you play and sing better.

A Page or Two of Reels!

The reel is undeniably the favourite dance tune with traditional players. Indeed it could be said to dominate the average 'session' to the extent that many other equally worthy forms of our Irish music are neglected.

The following three reels introduce the beginner to this popular dance. Take them slowly. Speed will come with practice. A nice style slowly played is better by far than speed without style!

Geehan's

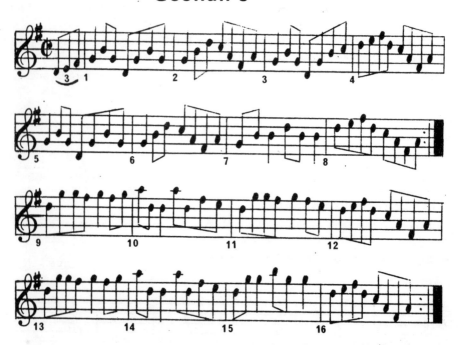

Geehan's: A straightforward reel in the key of 'G.' We have simplified it as much as possible. It is ideal for the beginner, being both easy and tuneful.

Sally Gardens: A little more complex. Listen to the pattern, the first part is in 'G' but the second introduces those minor sounds which add to the beauty and richness of our music.

Sonny Martin: A 'full blooded reel!' Very suitable for the fiddle. Listen carefully to the tune within a tune effect of the 'D', 'E', 'D', in bars 1, 5, 9, 10, 13, 14 and of 'E', 'F', 'E', in bars 3 and 11.

See how emphasising these notes adds to the overall rhythm of this reel. Never forget that reels are dance tunes and should be played with a strong 'bounce.'

The Sally Gardens

REEL

Sonny Martin

REEL

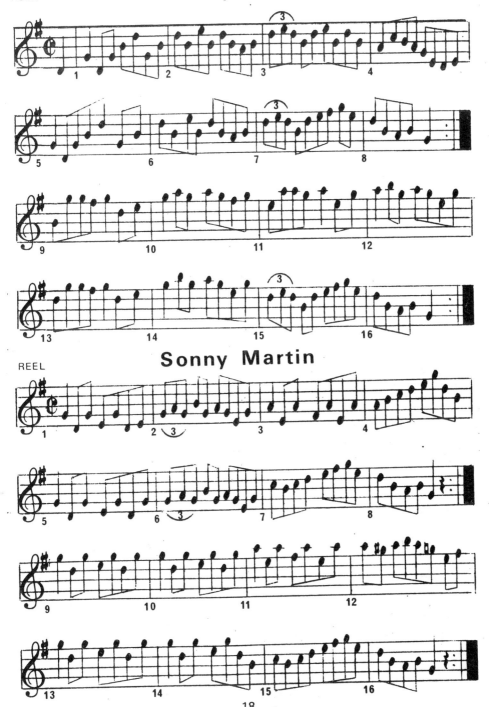

18

The Boyne Water

MARCH

AN 'ORANGE' TUNE

Captain Dunne's

Tyrone's Ditches

20

Matt Hylands

There was a lord, lived in this town,
Who had a lovely handsome daughter
She was courted by a fair young män
Who was a servant to her father.

But when her father came to know
He swore he'd send him from the island
The maid she knew that her heart would break,
Had she to part from young Matt Hylands.

So straight away, to his room she goes,
And orders him for to awaken.
Saying, "Rise my love and go away,
This very night you will taken,

Note 1. The pause marks over some of the bars indicate that the note below the mark is held out somewhat longer. The pause marks here are spaced in a regular pattern which gives the tune an added rhythm.

Note 2. Table 6, page 4, gives some information about dotted notes.

21

I overheard my father say,
In spite of me he would transport you,
So rise my love and go away,
You know right well I do adore you."

They both sat down upon the bed
Just for the space of one half hour
And not a word did either say
But down their cheeks the tears did shower.
She laid her head upon his breast,
And round his neck her arms entwined them.
"No lord nor duke nor earl I'll wed,
but wait for you my young Matt Hylands."

The lord he saw his daughter dear
one night alone as she lay crying,
"I'll give you leave to bring him back,
Since there's no one you love before him."

She wrote a letter then in haste,
For him her heart was still repining,
They brought him back, to the church they went,
And made a lord of young Matt Hylands.

ABOUT THIS SONG

This popular Ulster song seems to have first come to light around two hundred
years ago in Kilwarlin, near Moira, Co. Down. It was included in a collection
"Songs and Ballads in use in the Province of Ulster" by John and Abraham
Hume of Kilwarlin. The manuscript is in the National Library of Ireland. Around
1800 Gerald Griffin wrote a poem based on this song.

This version is based on the singing of Roisin White to whom we are indebted.

**Note 3. This or any other song in this collection can be lowered in pitch to suit
different voices by simply substituting a 'B flat,' or 'C' whistle for the 'D'
normally used. Use the same fingering, as most traditional musicians regard the
bottom note (fingering 6) of any whistle they play as being 'D.' This is a convenient
method of transposing (changing a tune from one key to another).**

Brian Boru's

Rogha Liadroma

Munster Buttermilk

24

Dingle Regatta

Dingle Regatta is an unforgettable experience. The wide bay, the billowing sails, the shouts of encouragement and the thrill of the little ships tearing through the waves are all captured in this lovely jig.

Note: Bars 17, 18, 21 and 22 may give some difficulty to beginners. Try playing only the first and fourth notes in each bar. So bars 17 and 18 have 'G', 'D', 'B', 'G', and bars 21 and 22 the same. Of course these notes must be held out longer, a full beat each, to keep to time.

25

Rose in the Heather

Gillian's Apples

The Kilfenora

JIG

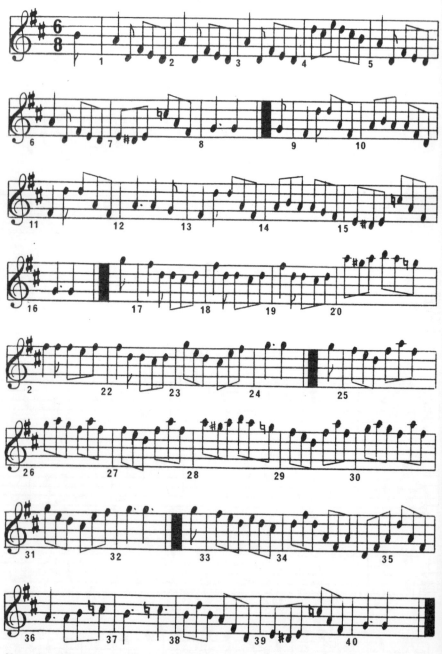

Note: Play 'G' sharp with 3 fingers on, only half covering the third hole. For 'D' sharp, 6 fingers on but half covering the sixth hole. Bars 20 and 28. The natural sign restores the 'G' following to normal.

27

REEL

The High Reel

REEL

The Flax in Bloom

28

The Four Poster Bed

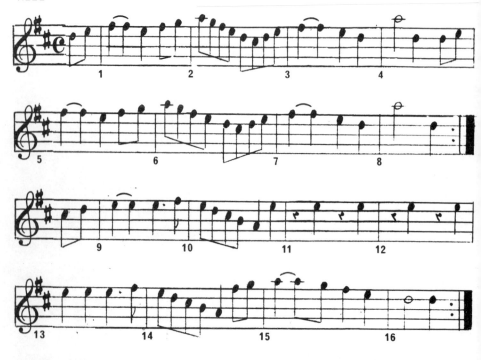

The Four Poster Bed: This is a very popular air around Gweedore in Donegal. The rests in bars 11 and 12 are accentuated by tapping the violin with the bow and shouting "Aon, Dó, Trí, Ceathair!"

Drowsy Maggie: Page 32. A circular or round reel where each part leads on to the next and back to the beginning with no apparent way of ending the tune naturally. In tunes like this the natural concluding note is supplied by the ear of the traditional musician. It is not always obvious. In this case it is 'E'.

Deirdre's Fancy

SLIP JIG

The Foxhunter

SLIP JIG

She was the Proud One

SLIP JIG

Dick Gossip's

REEL

Cooley's

REEL

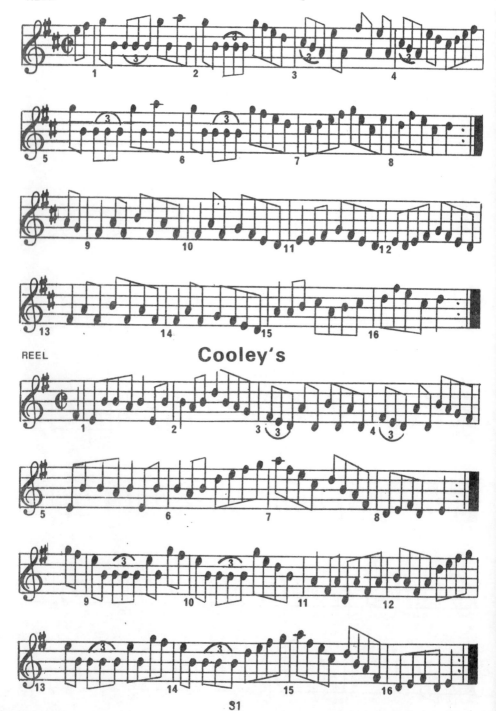

Drowsy Maggie

Jackie Coleman's

32

Bó na Leath Adhairce

Curfá:

Bó, bó, bó na leath adhairce
Bó bó sí an tseana chaor adharcach
Bó, bó, bó na leath adhairce
Bó dhroimfhionn dhearg is ní fheadar cá bhfaighinn í.

Thíos cois na toinne 'sea beathaíodh mo chaora
Ag Diarmuid Ó Díoláin ó Bharra na hAoine
Mac dearthár athar dom a chuir le faill í
Easpa tobac a bhí ar an gcladhaire.

Curfá.

NOTE

Note 1. It is just about impossible to set down in musical notation all the notes used in a song sung in the 'sean-nós' or traditional manner.

To listen to singers like Seosamh Ó hÉanaí is an education in itself.

Note 2. In bars six, nine and thirteen we show some of the ornamentation used by Mairéad Ní Mhaonaigh of Gweedore. We are indebted to her for this song.

33

B'fhearr liom ná scilling go bhfeicfinn mo chaora
'Teacht go dtí an doras ar maidin nó istoíche
Thálfadh sí bainne orm, bheathódh sí uan dom
Chuirfeadh sí jacketeen deas ar mo ghualainn.

Curfá.

Chonacsa beirithe í, chonac á roinnt í
Chuireas-sa dúil inti ach blaise ní bhfaighinn di
Ó nár dheas í, ó nár mheidhreach,
Ó nár dheas í an tseana chaor adharcach.

Curfá.

Dá mbeinnse i rachmas, i ngradam is in oidhreacht
Thabharfainnse giní ar chúpla sladhas di
Ó nár dheas í, ó nár mheidhreach,
Ó nár dheas í an tseana chaor adharcach.

Curfá.

D'íosfainn lán píce di, d'íosfainn lán oighin di
D'íosfainn stráice den tseana chaor adharcach
Ó nár dheas í, ó nár mheidhreach,
Ó nár dheas í an tseana chaor adharcach.

Curfá.

Gahan's

A PAIR OF HORNPIPES
No. 1

CHANGE OF KEY

2nd.

Dunphy's

No. 2

35

An Cailín Fionn

Chart six, page four, tells a little about dotted notes. Hornpipes are usually played in a slow heavy tempo with the first and third beats stressed in each bar. They abound in dotted notes which add to the characteristic sound.

For clarity's sake, we have not shown these dotted notes in our arrangements on page **35** opposite but, for example, bar seven of Dunphy's could be written like this. Notice that this helps the emphasis on the first and third beats mentioned above. Compare page **35** with page **71**.

1st BEAT   3rd

36

TWO FAVOURITES
JIG

Sackow's

JIG

The Lilting Fisherman

CHANGE KEY

The Hare in the Heather

A FOUR PART REEL

Úr-chnoc Chéin Mhic Cáinte

A phlúr na maighdean is úire gné,
'Fuair clú le scéimh ón Ádhamhchlainn,
A chúl na bpéarla, a rún na héigse,
'Dhúblas féile 's fáilte;
A ghnúis mar ghréin le dúscadh a' lae
A mhúchfadh léan le gáire,
'Sé mo chumha gan mé 's tú, a shiúr, linn féin
Sa dún sin Chéin Mhic Cáinte.

Táim brúite i bpéin, gan suan, gan néal
De do chumha, a ghéag is áille;
'S gur tú mo roghain i gcúigibh Éireann
A' chúis nach séanaim ás de;
Dá siúlfá, a réalt gan smúid, liom féin,
Ba súgach saor ár sláinte
Gheofá plúr is méad is cnuasach craobh
Sa dún sin Chéin Mhic Cáinte.

The beautiful music for this poem is credited to Peadar Ó Dubhda.

A chiúin-bhean tséimh na gcuachann péarlach,
Gluais liom féin ar ball beag,
Nuair bheas uaisle is cléir is tuataí i néal
In a suan faoi éadaí bána;
Ó thuaidh go mbéam i bhfad uafa araon
Teacht nua-chruth gréine amárach
Gan duais linn féin in uaigneas aerach
San uaimh sin Chéin Mhic Cáinte.

The author of this poem, Peadar Ó Doirnín, spent some of his life as a Hedge Schoolmaster in South Armagh.

Cnoc Chéin Mhic Cáinte is named after Cian, son of Cáinte, of Irish mythological fame. It tells of a lover's pleading with a loved one to flee with him.

The present name of the spot is Killen, about two miles North of Dundalk and Donal O'Sullivan's translation goes, "'Twere bliss with you, dear heart alone, on Killin's Hill of Faery."

The Nine Points of Roguery

The Ships are Sailing

41

The Hunt

We first heard 'The Hunt' at a fleadh in Listowel. Played softly and sweetly on two concertinas, it was as if we were listening to the music of some long gone age. The high natural 'F' in bar ten giving an almost faerie effect.

"Noble youths in glossy garments of smooth silk served drink in golden cups and, as Cuchulainn drank, the harpers and musicians gave forth sweet music and the very birds sang in tune with the music of the harps!"

From the Irish.

This reference in Irish mythology emphasises that love of music which has been characteristic of Ireland from the earliest times.

Cliffs of Doneen

SLOWLY

Once again I will wander from my own native home,
Far across the blue mountains, far away o'er the foam,
But in all of my rambles I never have seen,
Like the high rocky slopes round the cliffs of Doneen.

So farewell to Doneen, farewell for a while,
And to all the kind neighbours I am leaving behind,
To the cross roads and sand hills where lately I've been
On the high rocky slopes round the cliffs of Doneen.

Oh! how pleasant to wander on a bright summer's day,
Where the apples and cherries will never decay,
Where the hare and the rabbit no plainer can be seen
Making homes for their young ones round the cliffs of Doneen.

Take a view o'er the Shannon, strange sights you'll see there
You'll see high rocky mountains from the west coast of Clare
And the towns of Kilrush and Kilkee can be seen,
From the high rocky slopes round the cliffs of Doneen.

So farewell to Doneen, farewell for a while,
And although we are parted by the raging sea wild,
Once again I will wander with my Irish colleen,
Round the high rocky slopes of the cliffs of Doneen.

The Ballydesmond Polkas

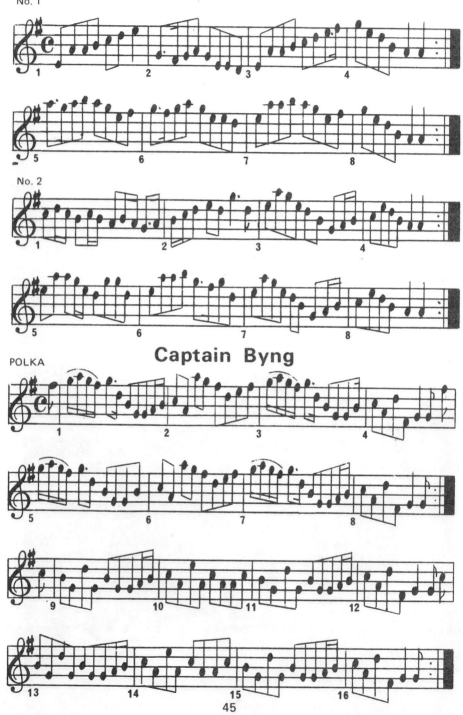

Captain Byng

45

The Kid on the Mountain

This very popular slip jig has been arranged here with some of the ornamentation commonly used shown in very small notes.

Try playing the tune over once or twice without these to get the feel of it. Then add them, taking care not to go out of time. Keep them light and unobtrusive.

You will notice that slip jigs tend to have three goups of three notes each per bar. Bar 6 above is an example. Nine-eight time has three emphasised beats per bar. In bar six these would come at the first note of each of the three groups. That is at 'G', 'D' and 'D'. The first beat is the strongest. See also the notes on page 11.

P.45 **Ballydesmond Polkas.** These lively tunes came to us from the Pipers' Club in Armagh. They are often played elsewhere with Bar 9 having the simplified form, crochet 'C', crochet 'B', crochet 'A', finishing with the 'G' 'A' that ends the bar.

P.45 **Captain Byng.** The Irish version of an old favourite. Play the first four notes of bars one, three, five and seven with a great flourish!

46

Harp Festival in the Assem

om, Belfast, 10-13 July 1792

Ag Úirchill An Chreagáin

Ag Úirchill a' Chreagáin sea chodail mé 'réir faoi bhrón,
Is le héirí na maid'ne tháinig ainnir fá mo dhéin le póig;
Bhí gríosghrua garth' aici 'gus loinnir ina céibh mar ór,
'S ba é íochshláinte 'n domhain a bheith 'g amharc ar a' ríoghan óig.

A fhialfhir charthanaigh, ná caitear thusa 'néalta bróin,
Ach éirigh go tapaidh agus aistrigh liom siar sa ród
Go tír dheas na meala nach bhfuair Galla inti réim go fóill,
'S gheobhair aoibhneas ar hallaí 'mo mhealladhsa le siamsa ceoil.

A ríoghan is deise 'n tú Hélen fár tréaghdadh slóigh
Nó'n de na naoi mná deasa Pharnassus thú 'bhí déanta i gcló?
Cá tír ins a' chruinne 'n ar hoileadh thú, a réalt gan ceo,
Le'r mian leat mo shamhailse bheith ' cogarnaigh leat siar sa ród?

49

Ná fiafraigh domsa 'n cheist sin nó ní chodlaím a' taobh seo 'en Bhóinn;
Is síogaí beag linbh mé a hoileadh le taobh Gráinne Óig'
I mbruíon cheart na n-ollamh bím go follas a' dúscadh 'n cheoil,
Bím san oíche ag Teamhair 's ar maidin i lár Thír Eoghain.

Sé mo ghéarghoin tinnis gur theastaigh uainn Gaeil Thír Eoghain,
Agus oidhrí an Fheadha gan seaghais faoi líg dár gcomhair
Géaga glandaite Néill Fhrasaigh nach dtréigfeadh 'n ceol
'S a chuirfeadh éideadh fá Nollaig ar na hollaimh a bheadh a géilleadh dóibh.

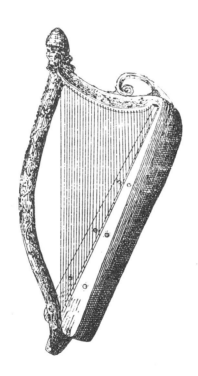

When Irish was more widely spoken in South Ulster than it is today, this song was so popular that in the early years of this century it was almost the national anthem of the area!

The author, Art MacCooey, who lived from circa 1738 until 1773, dying at the young age of 34, lived at Creggan in South Armagh.

We have already mentioned Ó Doirnín and must say also that this whole area of South Armagh had become a fertile ground for the cultivation of Irish literature at this time.

Doherty's

The Sligo Maid

Blind Mary

TURLOCH O' CAROLAN

The blind harper was born about 1670, near Nobber, Co. Meath. He may not have taken up the harp until blinded by smallpox at about sixteen years of age.

During his life as a wandering minstrel he composed some two hundred pieces of music. The first of these, 'Bridget Cruise' was prompted by his feelings for that young lady.

How many of these were inspired by older airs we do not know. But certainly 'Blind Mary' is in a very different vein from 'O'Carolan's Concerto,' page 57.

When he died, in 1738, a vast crowd of people assembled to pay tribute to him. He had in his early life been befriended by the McDermott Roe family and Mrs. McDermott Roe is reputed to have joined the mourners to, as she said, "weep over the poor gentleman."

Óró Mo Bháidín

Crochfa' mé seoíta 'gus gabhfa' me siaı,
Ó-ró! mo churraichín ó!
'S go hoíche Fhéil' Eoin ní thiocfa' mé 'niar,
Ó-ó-ró mo bháidín!

Curfá:

Ó-ró mo churraichín ó!
Ó-ró! mo bháidín
Ó-ó-ró! mo churraichín ó!
'S ó-ó-ró! mo bháidín!

'S nach breá í mo bháidín ag snámh ar an gcuan,
Óró mo churraichín ó,
'S na céaslaí á dtarraingt go láidir 's go buan
Ó-ó-ró mo bháidín!

Curfá.

'S nach éachtach a léimneach thar tonntracha ard',
Óró mo churraichín ó,
'S nach éadrom í 'iompar aníos thar an trá,
Ó-ó-ró mo bháidín!

Curfá.

'S nach lúfar í 'g iomramh soir agus siar,
Óró mo churraichín ó,
A sárú ní bhfaighidh tú ó Árainn go Cliar,
Ó-ó-ró mo bháidín!

Curfá.

Pádraig Mac Piarais.

Pádraig Mac Piarais, 1879-1916, was the author of a number of short stories, poems and plays in Irish. He was executed for his part in the 1916 rebellion.

In the days before powered craft were developed, the West coast of Ireland claimed many a sailing ship and her crew. The prevailing Westerly winds and frequent gales encouraged the development of the currach, a light, very seaworthy rowed boat. The Aran Islanders to this day perform remarkable feats of seamanship in these small vessels and our song tells of a man's affection for his little boat.

Cliffs of Moher

JIG

To stand on the cliffs of Moher in County Clare on a clear day is an unforgettable experience. Far below, the slow, relentless, surge of the sea thunders against the rocks, sending spray hundreds of feet into the air. Man is made to feel puny and insignificant.

Off shore lie the beautiful Aran Islands. From Dun Aongus, on Innishmore, Moher looks its true height. Across all those miles of sea the looming menace of those huge, brooding cliffs is an awesome sight.

That is the background to this fine jig. Fancifully, perhaps, one can hear the sentiments expressed above running through the tune.

"The music of the forest sang to Cuirithir and me, and the sound of the raging sea.
From the Irish.

The Ballyoran

HORNPIPE

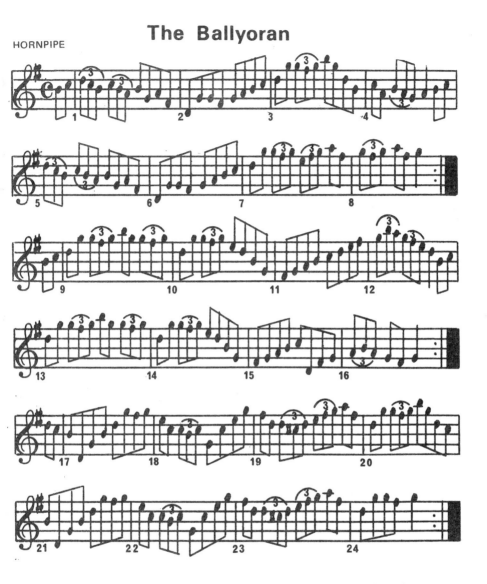

In this book we have the Ballyoran Polkas and, above, the Ballyoran Hornpipe.
As it happens, Ballyoran is the name of a district in Portadown where a lot of
the young members of Ceoltóirí Phort-an-Dúnáin live.

So, light-heartedly, we have claimed these tunes as our very own. But, of course,
there is more than one Ballyoran in Ireland!

O'Carolans Concerto

SOMETHING DIFFERENT!

Sí-Bhean Locha Léin

AIR

When we wrote about 'The Hunt' on page 42 we mentioned the music of a different age. Compare the lively 'O' Carolan's Concerto' with the grace and loneliness of 'Sí-Bhean Locha Léin.'

There are, perhaps, three types of Irish music present in this book. The various songs and airs, reels, jigs and hornpipes; the polkas; and O' Carolan's music.

Some would claim that O' Carolan's compositions and the polkas are not Irish in character and should not be included. We have some sympathy with this view, but feel that these tunes, if not Irish in construction, have become so by osmosis.

However, we remember a well known musician telling us after playing some polkas, that he had to 'think himself back into' a reel again.

So we impress upon the beginner the need to 'feel' his way right into the heart of the music of our country.

To those brought up away from the sound of Traditional Music it has first to be recognised and then learnt as a separate art form.

Éamonn an Chnoic

SLOWLY

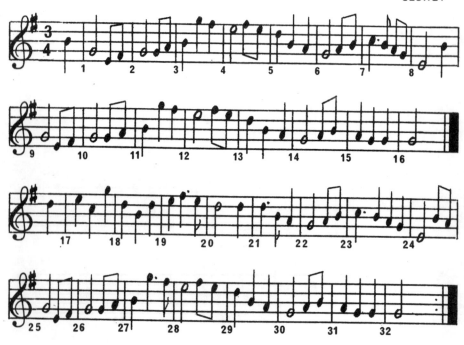

Cé hé sin amuigh
A bhfuil faobhar ar a ghuth,
Ag réabadh mo dhorais dúnta?
Mise Éamonn a' Chnoic
Ata báite fuar fliuch
Ó shíorshiúl sléibhte 's gleannta!
A lao dhil 's a chuid,
Cad a dhéanfainnse dhuit,
Muna gcuirfinn ort beinn dem' ghúna,
'S go bhfuil púdar go tiubh
Dá shíorshéideadh leat,
'S go mbeimis araon múchta.

This air is the one generally sung. Not the original, it is credited to Margaret Hannagan, and was first sung by her at the Oireachtas in 1901 where it won first prize.

Is fada mise amuigh
Faoi shneachta is faoi shioc
'S gan dánacht agam ar aon neach;
Mo sheisreach gan scor,
Mo bhranar gan cur
Is gan iad agam ar aon chor!
Níl caraid agam
Is danaid liom san,
Do ghlacfadh mé moch ná déanach
'S go gcaithfidh mé dul
Thar farraige soir,
Ó is ann ná fuil aon dem' ghaoltaibh.

A chumann 's a shearc,
Raghaimidne seal
Fá choillte na measa gcumhra,
Mar a bhfaighimid an breac,
'S an lon ar a nead,
An fia 'gus an poc ag búireach;
Na héiníní binne
Ar ghéigíní a' seinnm,
Is an cuaichín ar bharr an iúir ghlais;
Go brách brách ní thiocfaidh
An bás inár ngoire
I lár na coille cumhra.

Born at Knockmeoll Castle, Co. Tipperary, Edmund Ryan became, in the tumult
of Ireland in the late sixteen hundreds, dispossessed of his land and found himself
with a price on his head.

Soldier, adventurer, rapparee and poet, he tells here of seeking shelter and of the
girl who befriends him.

60

The Yellow Heifer

The Pigeon on the Gate

61

McMahon's

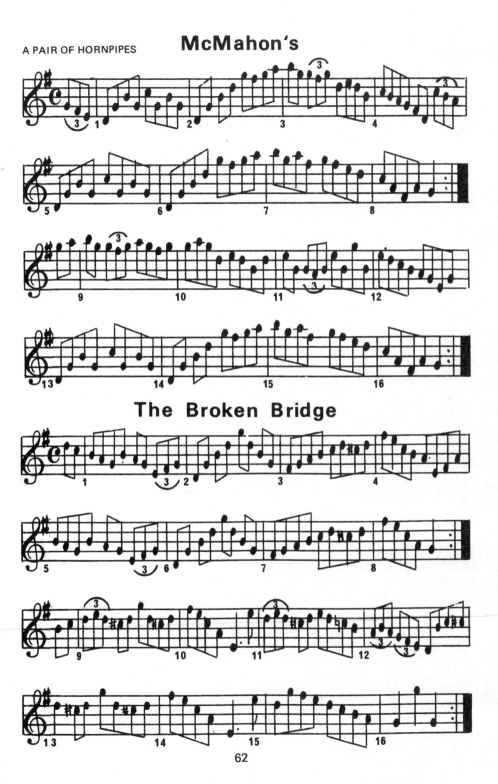

The Broken Bridge

Gleanntáin Ghlas' Ghaoth Dobhair

Céad slán ag sléibhte maorga Chontae Dhún na nGall,
Agus dhá chéad slán ag an Eargal ard in a stua os cionn caor is coll;
Nuair a ghluais mise thart le Loch Dhún Lúich' go ciúin sa ghleann ina luí
I mo dhiaidh bhí gleanntáin ghlas' Ghaoth Dobhair, is beag nár bhris mo chroí.

Ag taisteal dom amach trí chnoic Ghleann Domhain 's an Mhucais ar mo chúl
Ní miste dom 'rá le brón 's le crá gur frasach a shil mise súil;
Go Meiriceá siar a bhí mo thriall i bhfad thar an fharraige mhór.
D'fhág mé slán ar feadh seal' ag Dún na nGall is ag gleanntáin ghlas' Ghaoth
    Dobhair.

Slán, slán go fóill, a Dhún na nGall, a chontae shéimh gan smál,
Is do d'fheara breáth' in am an ghá nár umhlaigh riamh roimh Ghall;
Tá áit i mo chroí do gach fear 's gach mnaoi, is gach páiste beag agus mór
Atá beo go buan gan bhuairt gan ghruaim fá ghleanntáin ghlas' Ghaoth
    Dobhair.

Proinsias Ó Maonaigh.

The illustration shows people gathering seaweed and edible shellfish
on Inishbofin island in Famine times.

Today, the people of the Donegal Gaeltacht are self-sufficient in
many ways and have a pride in themselves and in things Irish that
sets an example to the rest of Ireland.

Our song tells of the poets love of that area.

Bunclody

Oh were I at the moss house, where the birds do increase,
At the foot of Mount Leinster or some silent place,
By the streams of Bunclody where all pleasures do meet,
And all I would ask is one kiss from you sweet.

If I was a clerk and could write a good hand,
I would write my true love a letter that she might understand
For I am a young fellow who is wounded in love,
Once I lived in Bunclody, but now must remove.

T is why my love slights me, as you may understand,
That she has a freehold and I have no land,
She has great store of riches, and a large sum of gold,
And everything fitting a house to uphold.

So fare you well father and my mother, adieu
My sister and brother farewell unto you,
I am bound for America my fortune to try,
When I think of Bunclody I'm ready to die.

Ballyoran Polkas

Pretty Maggie Morrissy

Ding Dong Dederó

Ding dong dederó, buail sin, séid seo!
Ding dong dederó, buail sin, séid seo!
Ding dong dederó, buail sin, séid seo!
D'imigh mo bhean leis an táilliúir aerach.

Ní maith a ním féin tua ná corrán,
Ní maith a ním féin ramhan ná sleán,
Ó d'imigh uaim mo stuaire mná
Le gaige trua gan bhuar, gan sparán.

A bhean úd thíos an bhrollaigh ghléigil,
B'fhearra dhuit fille is na builg do shéide
Ná do ghabha maith féin go bráth a thréigean
Is triall ris an táilliúir ar fuaid na h-Éireann.

**Note: 'D.C. al Fine' means go back to the beginning and play to
'Fine'. This completes the tune.**

Cá bhfuil mo bhuachaill? Buail sin, séid seo!
Cá bhfuil mo neart, is snas mo chéirde?
Cá bhfuil mo radharc? Tá'n adharc ar m'éadan
Ó d'éaluigh mo bhean leis an táilliúir aerach.

Ding dong dederó, buail sin, séid seo!
Ding dong dederó, buail sin, séid seo!
D'imigh mo bhean leis an táilliúir aerach,
Is ní thúrfadh mo chosa mé ar sodar fad téide.

Very few songs of occupation have come down to us in Ireland.
There are two or three versions of this Blacksmith's Song; all
cnaracterised by the ring of the hammers on the anvil implied
in the line, "Ding, Dong, Dedero."

Scent of the Bog

The Cuckoo

The Ship in Full Sail

The Hag with the Money

JIG

CHANGE KEY

72

De Bharr na gCnoc

Ó seal do bhíos im' mhaighdean shéimh
Is anois im' bhaintreach chaite, thréith,
Tá mo chéile ag treabhadh na dtonn go tréan
De bharr na gcnoc is in imigéin.

Curfá:

Is é mo rogha é a thoghas dom féin
Is maith an domhain go dtabharfainn é
D'fhonn é bheith ar bord ar long gan baol
De bharr na gcnoc is in imigéin.

Go bhfeiceadsa an lá, a stór mo chléibh,
'Na mbeidh cloig dá mbualadh is droim dá léas,
Do ghalltromp' ag gabháil gach áitribh réidh
De bharr na gcnoc is in imigéin.

Curfá.

Go bhfeiceadsa coróin ar stór mo chléibh
Do thógfaidh ceo is brón de Ghaeil,
Gach rí atá san domhan go léir
Ag umhlú dó le cúnamh Dé.

Curfá.

Ó suífead síos ar chnoc go hard
Is gheobhadh go córach cleite im' láimh
Má gheibhim téimheal go scríobhadh mo sháith
Ar ghníomhartha suilt is ar mhaith mo ghra.

Seán Clárach Mac Domhnaill.

**Note. This beautiful air sounds so well when played by whistles
and fiddles together that we have arranged it in the key of 'D'.
This suits the whistle very well but is rather high for singing to.
Try singing it in the key of 'B flat.' See note 3, page 22.**

Slieve Gallen Braes

As I went a-walking one morning in May,
To view yon fair valleys and mountains so gay,
I was thinking on those flowers, all doomed to decay,
That bloom around ye, bonny, bonny, Slieve Gallen braes.

How oft in the morning with my dog and my gun,
I roamed through the glens for joy and for fun,
But those days are now all over and I must go away,
So farewell unto ye, bonny, bonny, Slieve Gallen braes.

How oft of an evening and the sun in the West,
I roved hand in hand with the one I loved best;
But the hopes of youth are vanished and now I'm far away,
So farewell unto ye, bonny, bonny, Slieve Gallen braes.

O! it was not the want of employment at home,
That caused us poor exiles in sorrow to roam,
But those tyrannising landlords, they would not let us stay
So farewell unto ye, bonny, bonny, Slieve Gallen braes.

Note. Listen to the effect produced by the notes in bar 14.
By shortening the first note of each pair we produce a characteristic Northern Irish or Scottish sound. This is borne out also
by the use of Scottish dialect words like 'Braes' and 'bonny.'

Airde Chuain

'Á mbeinn féin in Airde Chuain
In aice an tsléibhe 'tá bhfad uaim,
Ba annamh liom gan dul ar cuairt
Go gleann na gcuach, Dé Domhnaigh.

Curfá:

Och, ach, 'Éa' raí — agus ó!
'Éa'raí, lean dom — agus ó!
Sé mo chroí 'tá troimseach, brónach!

Is iomaí Nollaig a bhí mé féin
I mBun Abhann Doinne is mé gan chéill,
Ag iomáin ar a' trá bhán
'S mo chamán bán 'mo dhorn liom.

Curfá.

Note. Often translated as 'The Quiet Land of Erin' this song tells of
an exile gazing across from Scotland to the distant Irish coast. The
illustration shows Carrickfergus Castle many years ago.

Nach tuirseach mise anseo liom péin
Nach n-airím guth coiligh, lon dubh ná traon'?
Gealbhan, smólach, naoscach féin,
'S chan aithním péin a' Domhnach!

Curfá.

Sé seo an choraíocht 'tá buan;
Ar a' tsaol go gcuirfeadh sé cluain;
Mheallfadh sé an chaora ón uan —
Agus mheall sé uaimse an óige.

Curfá.

'Á mbeadh agam coite 's rámh
D'iomairfinn liom ar dhroim a' tsnáimh,
'S mé 'dúil as Dia go sroichfinn slán
'S go bhfaighinn bás in Éirinn.

Curfá.

The Princess Royal

O'CAROLAN

LULLABY

Dia Do Bheatha

REEL

Off in the Morning
Arranged for Tenor Banjo.

Lament

Marbhna Luimni

This beautiful haunting lament is heard in several versions. In this version the various pairs of quavers have the last note of the pair lengthened and the first note shortened. This is in contrast to the normal Irish custom of dotting the first note and shortening the second. Compare this tune with 'The Hunt' page 43.

Although this arrangement gives the tune a Scottish flavour the Irish musician plays it with many lightly and rapidly executed cuts and rolls (page 82).

Ornamentation

The newcomer to **Irish Traditional Music** must first accept that it has many points of difference with Western art or classical music. It can be said that the instinctive tendency of a musician with art musical training is to 'hear' harmonies in music. But it is true to say that the Irish traditional musician tends to 'hear' ornamentation in the music as he plays.

For instance on page 43 we have the song, 'The Cliffs of Doneen,'' Bars seven and eleven could be played exactly the same but the **grace notes, B and A** have been added to the 'G' in bar eleven. This is a simple form of ornamentation.

Using the above example, the note 'A' could be varied by playing 'A', 'B', 'A', 'G', 'A'. The notes 'B' and 'G' being very short and lightly played. This form of ornamentation is called a **roll on 'A'.**

Still on 'A', try playing 'A', 'C', 'A', again, the middle note is quickly and lightly played. This is called a **cut on 'A'.**

The table below gives some examples.

CHART ELEVEN   **Some examples of cuts.**

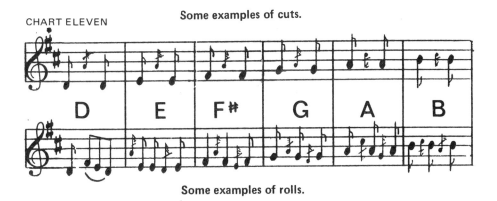

Some examples of rolls.

'C' and 'C sharp' are normally not elaborated on.

The table shows the ornamental notes much smaller than the main notes. These small notes should be played lightly, quickly and with just a flick of the finger.

Ornamentation varies from place to place. Whelan's jig, page 47, has several dotted crochets which pipe, whistle and flute players often roll. Yet we have heard many Northern fiddle players play these dotted notes as three sharply sounded quavers, 'E' for example, becoming 'E', 'E', 'E'. This gives the tune a totally different sound.

But whatever the form of embellishment used, learn to exercise and appreciate **good taste!**

Some Records of Interest

TITLE	COMPANY	NUMBER
Ag Úirchill An Chreagáin	Gael-Linn	C.E.S. 015
Airde Chuain	Gael-Linn	C.E.F. 031
Brian Boru's March	Philips	6392013
Blind Mary	E.M.I.	Stal (1) 1004
Bó Na Leath Adhairce	Gael-Linn	C.E.F.S. 027
Cliffs of Doneen	C.C.E.	Fleadh Cheoil 1970
Cooley's	Gael-Linn	C.E.F. 033
Cailín Fionn	C.C.E.	C.L. 2
Cuckoo	Shaskeen	OS-361
Captain Byng	Outlet	1017 B
Ding Dong Dederó	Gael-Linn	C.E.F. 016
Drowsy Maggie	Claddagh	C.C.14
Doherty's	Trailer	L.E.R. 2086
Don Oíche Úd i mBeithil	Outlet	1017 B
Éamonn An Chnoic	Gael-Linn	45 G.L.9
Gillian's Apples	Claddagh	C.C.7
Hunt	E.M.I. Stal (1)	1002
Hare in the Heather	Claddagh	C.C.14
High Reel	Gael-Linn	C.E.F. 013
Kid on the Mountain	Gael-Linn	C.E.F. 033
Kilfenora	E.M.I. Stal (1)	1,013
Lilting Fisherman	Dolphin Dolb	7016
Munster Buttermilk	Claddagh	C.C.5
Nine Points of Roguery	Trailer	L.E.R. 2086
Óró Mo Bháidín	Gael-Linn	C.E.F. 029
Rogha Liadroma	C.C.E.	C.L.2
Siún Ní Dhuibhir	Philips	6392013
Sally Gardens	Dolphin Dolb	7016
Ships are Sailing	Master Collector Series	N.Y. Vol. 1, 1974
Ship in Full Sail	Gael-Linn	C.E.F. 010
Scent of the Bog	Shaskeen	OS-361
Úr-chnoc Chéin Mhic Cáinte	Gael-Linn	C.E.F. 026

Some tunes may have more than one title. The cuckoo is on Shaskeen as Murray's Fancy.' 'The Hare in the Heather' is a version of 'The Morning Dew,' etc.

About Instruments

The correct choice of instruments is very important. Generally speaking, insofar as Irish traditional music is concerned, instruments can be divided into four types.

In a category of their own so far as popularity and suitability is concerned we have the **Uilleann Pipes, Flute, Fiddle** and the **Whistle**. Because the player can easily vary the pitch of a note on these instruments the full beauty of Irish music can be expressed. Ornamentation becomes more subtle and forms of ornamentation can be employed which are not possible on some of the instruments mentioned below.

Then we have the **Harp**, which, quite simply, is in a class of its own.

Next we have the **Concertina** and **Two-Row Button Accordian.** It is not possible to vary the pitch of these instruments and the shrill tuning popular for accordians today tends to give these instruments a somewhat strident effect. In the hands of a sensitive player the concertina can be a very suitable instrument for Irish music whilst the popularity of the Two-Row Button Accordian is undoubted. For Irish music the B.C. tuning is the most popular Two-Row system. The Anglo-Type Concertina is to be preferred to the English-Type.

Then we have the **Piano** and **Continental Chromatic Accordians,** the **Piano,** the various **Mandolins** and **Banjos,** etc. The Piano is mostly used as an accompaniment to solo or group playing. The other instruments have become very popular in recent years. Some very good music is played on them and, in group playing, the additional tone colours introduced often enrich the effect.

And what player does not appreciate the 'lift' given to his music by a skilful pianist or accordeonist, the bass serving to bring out and display the beautiful chords hidden in our Irish music.

For dancing, too, the accordian gives 'body' to a Ceili Band and in the hands of a good player, is an attractive solo instrument.

On the following pages we give charts of some of the instruments mentioned. The whistle chart is at the front of the book. We feel that every one interested in Irish music should learn to play this versatile but inexpensive little instrument.

No chart is given of the **Flute**, the whistle player finding little difficulty in learning it. The Wooden Simple System Flute with one or more keys is the most popular.

84

The Mandolin and Violin

FINGERING

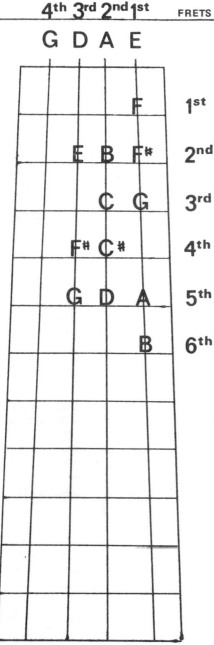

MANDOLIN

The 'D' and 'G' scales have the same fingering on violin and mandolin. Using the string name and the fret number as a guide, we get a 'D' scale as follows:-

D = D open string, E = D2, F$^\sharp$ = D4, G = D5, A = open A string, B = A2, C$^\sharp$ = A4, D' = A5.

The scale of G is similar:-

G = D5, A = A open string, B = A2, C = A3, D' = A5, E' = E open string, F$^\sharp$' = E2, G' = E3.

VIOLIN OR FIDDLE

The fiddle is one of the most popular of the instruments used in Ireland. It is tuned in the same way as the mandolin, but the notes are produced by drawing a bow across the strings, which are single.

Unlike the mandolin, the positions of the notes are not marked by frets. There is nothing to stop the beginner using the mandolin chart as a guide and placing 'frets,' made from strips of 'sellotape' on the finger-board of the violin.

It is much better to seek the advice of a good fiddler.

Use a little instrument called a pitch-pipe and **keep your instrument in tune.**

The Button Accordian

CHART THIRTEEN

This very popular instrument come in various tunings. The most commonly used one in Ireland has the inner row tuned in the key of 'C.' The outer in the key of 'B.'

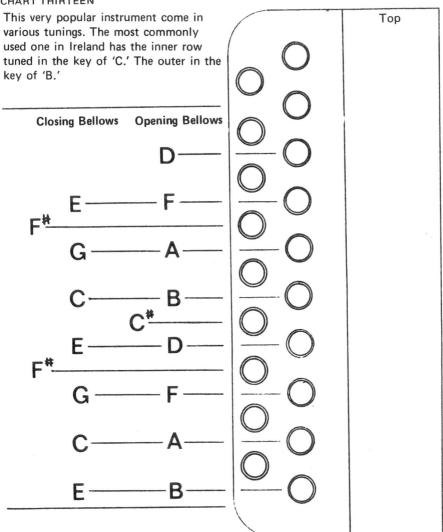

Top

Closing Bellows   Opening Bellows

D

E —— F

F#

G —— A

C —— B

C#

E —— D

F#

G —— F

C —— A

E —— B

Depending on the instrument 'D' is the tnird or fourth button down in the inside row. Only the notes for the keys of 'G' and 'D' have been picked out for simplicity's sake, plus 'F' natural which strays into Irish music with a very nice effect. Almost all of the tunes in this book can be played on the notes given.

Good bellows control is very important, never play loudly but practise smooth playing in a quiet manner. Listen to the best players!

The Tenor Banjo

FINGERING

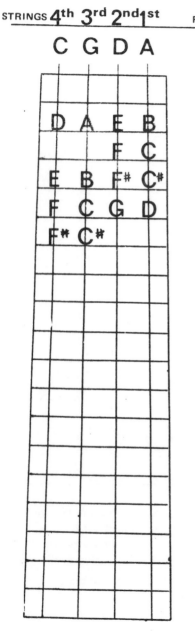

STRINGS 4th 3rd 2nd 1st FRETS

C G D A

In the banjo family, the tenor seems to be the most widely preferred for traditional music.

1st Only the notes of the 'G' and 'D' scales

2nd are shown on the chart, plus 'F' natural which is needed occasionally.

3rd

4th Using the names of the strings, 'C', 'G' 'D', 'A', as a guide together with the fret numbers we get a 'D' scale as

5th follows:-

6th D = C2, E = C4, F$^\#$ = C6
G is open third string,
A = G2, B = G4, C$^\#$ = G6
D' is open second string,
E' = D2, F$^{\#}$' = D4, G' = D5
A' is open first string,
B' = A2, C$^\#$' = A4, D^2 = A5.

This gives us two octaves of the 'D' scale. Chart three, page two, gives the notes of the 'g' scale.

Using this guide, most of the tunes in the book can be played.

Needless to say, help should be sought from all experienced traditional player. Listen to records and tapes and **always** keep your instrument in tune. Use a set of pitch pipes for this.

30 Keyed Anglo Concertina

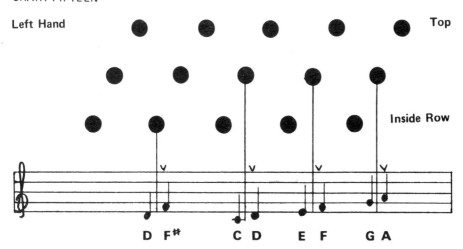

Left Hand   Top

                                                                    Inside Row

D F#   C D   E F   G A

V = Bellows opening. Note, C# is sometimes opposite direction.

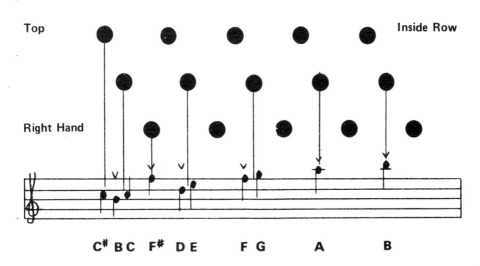

Top   Inside Row

Right Hand

C# B C F# D E   F G   A   B

The middle row of buttons on each side is the basic row. The beginner should master some simple tunes on the middle row only going to the other rows for F# and C#.

The other rows contain alternative notes, playable usually by using the bellows in the opposite direction to that required for the same note on the basic row. The little finger of the left hand is used for F#

Uilleann Pipes

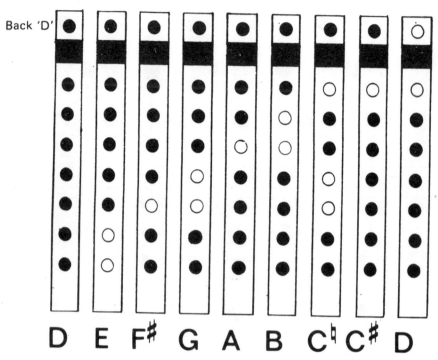

Back 'D'

D E F♯ G A B C♮ C♯ D

Raise 'A' to get richer 'C' sharp.

The holes to be left open are marked O. Holes to be closed are marked ●. The piper often wears a pad of leather above the right knee called a popping strap. Except when sounding the bottom note the chanter normally rests on this.

There are three drones, which sound continuously, and three regulators fitted with keys in a full set of pipes. The regulators can be played by a movement of the wrist and give a simple chord accompaniment.

89

Chanter Scale

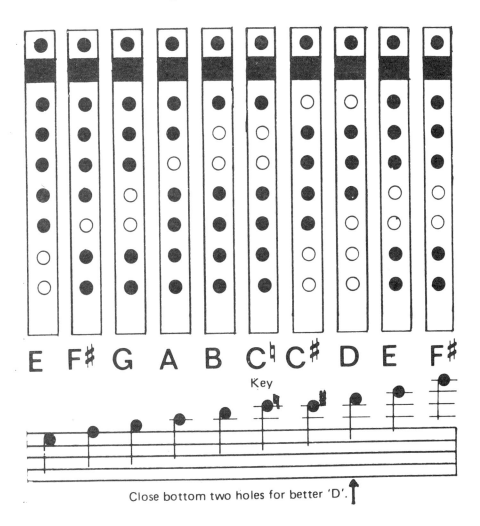

Close bottom two holes for better 'D'.

To the unknown genius who invented the pipes we owe a great debt. They are very difficult to obtain today and the best advice we can give a lucky new owner is to seek out a good piper and learn from him.

We give details of some books on pipes in the bibliography.

There is a very grave danger at the present time that the very art itself of making pipes will be lost.

Bibliography

The Pipers' Club, Armagh.

'Learn to Play the Tin Whistle,' an excellent series of three books. With well chosen tunes and basic instruction.

Comhaltas Ceoltóirí Éireann, Dublin.

'Tutor for the Feadóg Stáin,' comprehensive and clear notes on theory and ornamentation. Some excellent arrangements of tunes.

'Treoir,' the magazine of C.C.E., carries articles on all aspects of Irish music, including piping.

O'Neill, Waltons Ltd., Dublin.

'The Dance Music of Ireland, (1001 gems),' every musician should have what has become known as 'The Book.'

Breandán Breathnach, Dublin.

'Ceol Rinnce na hÉireann,' a very useful collection with many notes and references.

'Folk Music and Dances of Ireland,' a compact, readable little book, packed with information, including notes on piping.

P. McNulty, Glasgow.

'Dance Music of Ireland,' a selection worth having.

Nollaig OhUromoltaigh. Béal Feirste.

'Ceolta Uladh,' a nice little collection of songs with words and music in three books.

Peadar O' Rafferty, Belfast.

'The Irish Folk Dance Book,' a series of books giving the dance steps and figures for some Irish dances. With some music.

An Coimisiún le Rinncí Gaelacha.

'Ar Rinncidhe Fóirne', again a series giving instructions on various figure dances, and with music.

We list only a few of the publications available. There are many others, some out of print but still obtainable through libraries, etc.